PRAIRIE DOG

SCREECH OWL

RABBIT TRACKS

RUFFED GROUSE

WHITE-TAILED DEER

BEAVER

GREAT HORNED OWL

RED FOX

WOOD DUCK

00295
008014

RACCOON TRACKS

REDHEADED WOODPECKER

MEADOWLARK

BASS SUNFISH

FIELD MOUSE

BLUEBIRD

STRIPED SKUNK

WOODCHUCK

BOX TURTLE

PORCUPINE

BROWN TROUT

BLACK BEAR

RATTLESNAKE

FLICKER

RED SQUIRREL

ANIMAL SIGNS AND SIGNALS

Elk bugling

By Ted S. Pettit:

ANIMAL SIGNS AND SIGNALS
THE BOOK OF SMALL MAMMALS
THE WEB OF NATURE

Blue Jay

ANIMAL SIGNS AND SIGNALS

By TED S. PETTIT

Illustrated by G. DON RAY

Doubleday & Company, Inc.
Garden City, N.Y.
1961

Gray
Squirrel

Song Sparrow

THANKS

Our sincerest appreciation and gratitude is extended to Dr. E. Laurence Palmer, Professor Emeritus of Nature, Science and Conservation Education at Cornell University and author of *Fieldbook of Natural History*. Dr. Palmer reviewed and checked the manuscript and drawings and was tremendously helpful in suggesting improvements.

Herring Gull

CONTENTS

Horseshoe Crab

3033

Moonsnail

Whelk

Red squirrel chattering angrily

1 ANIMAL COMMUNICATIONS

Ever since man first appeared on earth he has found it necessary for one reason or another to be able to read and understand animal signs, sounds, and other signals. Early man depended to a large extent upon wild animals for food and clothing. His life depended upon his being able to follow tracks and trails to find the animals he needed.

In turn, he too was often followed by some animals, and to escape with his life he found it important to develop skill in reading the signs of nature. Even today in some of the more remote parts of the earth many human beings must be skillful in understanding animal signals and the messages they carry. They still depend upon wild animals for part of their food, clothing or livelihood.

For most of us, however, an understanding of the signs of the wild is no longer a matter of necessity. But it may be important in our job or hobby. There are many people to whom this knowledge is still important and, on occasion, their lives may depend upon their skill.

During World War II thousands of pilots were trained in survival techniques and in living off the land. Should they be forced down in a wilderness or a near-wilderness area they could well depend upon wild animals for food and survival.

Left: Black bear leaves a sign on tree

Bullfrog

Many people too have professions or jobs that require ability and training in understanding animal signs and signals. Naturalists, biologists, wildlife conservationists, hunting and fishing guides, trappers, commercial fishermen and others must be able to read signs of nature and interpret correctly what they see, hear, touch, taste or smell.

On the hobby side, amateur naturalists, hunters, fishermen, nature photographers, hikers, campers, wilderness travelers and gardeners all get much more enjoyment in the outdoors and gain a greater appreciation of the world of nature if they, too, learn how and why animals send and receive the messages they do.

Wild animals communicate with each other and with man for different reasons and in different ways. Many animals make sounds of one sort or another to express fear, anger, contentment, warning, or other feelings or attitudes. Others leave visual or scent signs that may indicate some or all of these same feelings. Some animals, too, have visual signals to send a message, and touch and taste messages may also be used. When we know the reasons why animals communicate with each other and the methods involved, we can understand more quickly what animals are doing and some of the reasons they act as they do.

Many times animal communications are entirely accidental. The animal had no intention of leaving a message. The rabbit that nibbled lettuce or cabbage in a garden may leave a scent trail on the ground which a dog or fox may follow. Certainly the chewed leaves and droppings tell the gardener that a rabbit was there. The muskrat or raccoon that invades a cornfield and eats young corn also leaves unmistakable, yet accidental, signs that it was there. The animal did not intend to advertise its presence, or even its existence.

Many animal signs, on the other hand, do show some degree of intent, since the animal has control over whether or not it sends a message. A wild turkey or a quail may give a sound signal to warn its young that danger threatens. The young run for cover or remain motionless until a second sound signal indicates that all is well and that the brood may once again feed safely.

Skunks exercise remarkable control, many times, over their well-known defensive weapon. They use it, it seems, only as a last resort when other warnings fail. But when necessary, they use it effectively to fight off an enemy.

Other animal signals or signs are the result of instinct. They are much like your reaction to a loud and unexpected noise, such as a door slamming or a car backfiring. You flinch or jump. A deer may flash its white tail, a beaver may slap the water with its broad tail, or a rattlesnake may strike. The sight, sound or touch signal sent by the animal is the result of an instinctive reaction rather than intent on the part of the animal.

It is important that we understand how and why animals send and receive messages so that as we intercept them we may read them accurately. It is all too easy to be led astray by signs of nature and to draw inaccurate conclusions based on what we see, hear, or smell. Too often we tend to give an animal credit for power of thought or for intentions that it does not possess. Too often we interpret what we see in terms of our own thought processes and experiences. As we try to interpret animal signals we must be careful not to assume a power of reasoning and thought that does not exist.

Thus the purpose of this book is to show in picture and text many of the more common animal signs, sounds, and other signals through which we can discover more about what animals are doing. Many wild animals are wary of man. Many, too, are active only at night. Much of the time the only evidence of their existence is a track or other sign they leave in passing. By being able to identify signs and understand signals which we see, hear, feel, smell, or taste, we can find out which animals live in any given area and a little of how they live. Many of the signs and signals discussed here may be observed in any park, suburban yard, wooded area or field near town, or a nearby pond, lake, marsh, or sea beach. Only a very few are made by animals that inhabit the wilder parts of this continent, and they are included because of special features of one sort or another. This book is limited, too, chiefly to the higher forms of animals—those with central nervous systems and internal skeletons—some of the fishes, reptiles, amphibians, birds, and mammals. Other animals mentioned are incidental to the discussion.

Being able to read the signs of the wild is fun itself. It is a fascinating hobby and one that knows no particular season, time, or place. Skill in this field may easily contribute greater enjoyment and success in other outdoor hobbies. Let's look now at some ways in which a few animals communicate with their own kind, with other animals, and with man.

Timber Rattler

Beaver Lodge

Muskrat Houses

Grebe on Nest

Bluegill on Nest

2   DENS, NESTS, BURROWS

When animals build homes of one kind or another, they certainly do not intend that these homes should be a form of communication. They are not trying to send a message to another animal. Most of the time they try to conceal their nest or burrow so that it will not be seen or found. For animal homes, generally, are places to raise young in safety, to store food for the winter, or to seek protection from enemies or weather.

However, animal dens, nests, and burrows are unmistakable animal signs and many times are the only evidence of an animal's presence. There is much we can tell about an animal and how it lives by a close examination of its home.

Some animal homes, such as beaver houses, woodchuck burrows, or eagle nests are reasonably permanent. The animal builds its home and uses it as long as it lives, unless the home is destroyed by man, fire, or other accident.

Other animals—most of the birds, for example—build a new nest each year and use it for a short time only. Birds may come back year after year to the same place to nest, but they rarely use an old nest.

Animal homes, generally, are as distinctive as the animal itself. Once you get to know them you do not have to see the animal to know that it lives or has lived in the area.

11

Hole in the Ground

Many different kinds of animals, from skinks to skunks and from bats to badgers, live in holes in the ground. There are reptiles and amphibians, birds and mammals that dig their own burrows or use burrows made by other animals. Even catfish use underwater holes in river banks as places to lay their eggs.

By looking at a hole in the ground you can usually tell quickly what kind of animal made it. But you cannot always tell what kind of animal may be using the hole at the time you find it. For rabbits and skunks sometimes move into abandoned woodchuck holes and take them over as their own. Burrowing owls and rattlesnakes may occupy a prairie dog or badger burrow for a short time or long—depending upon the badger.

Some of the more common animals that live in burrows in the ground are: tiger salamander, spadefoot toad, some lizards, gopher tortoises, box turtles, many of the snakes, birds, such as kingfishers, bank and rough-winged swallows, and many mammals, including chipmunks, moles, mice, rats, gophers, ground squirrels, foxes, mink, weasels and armadillos.

The size, shape, and location of a burrow are usually the identifying marks that help tell you what kind of animal made it. Sometimes animal or plant remains upon which the animal feeds may be found nearby that also help in identification. Then, too, you can tell whether the burrow is a permanent or temporary home by looking around the outside. Animals such as some of the reptiles and amphibians that dig a burrow only as a place to raise young use it for a short time, and there will be little, if any, indication on the ground around that there is an animal in the hole. But woodchucks, foxes, ground squirrels, or prairie dogs that use a burrow permanently usually have runways leading to it that are quite evident.

An easy way to discover whether a burrow is occupied is this: Get five or six pencil-sized sticks, sharpened on one end. Poke them in the ground just far enough so that they stand upright at the burrow entrance. Check in a day or so to see if they have been disturbed.

Gopher Tortoise

Flying Squirrel

Holes in Trees

A large, dead, hollow tree in the forest or woodland edge may almost resemble an apartment house for wild animals. Many different kinds live in tree cavities.

If the tree is rotted out at the base close to the ground, a bear may find the hole suitable for winter hibernation. Or a raccoon, porcupine, opossum, or a mouse may find what it needs for a place to raise its young or find protection.

Higher up in the same tree may be a woodpecker hole made this year and occupied by any one of several birds of this family. There may be an old woodpecker hole made last year or years ago that now has been taken over by a chickadee, nuthatch, crested flycatcher, or even a screech owl.

If the hole is large enough and there is water nearby, a woodduck may move in and build its nest, or a great horned owl may find the hole to its liking. On the other hand, the same tree cavity could be occupied by a squirrel, a raccoon, a deer mouse, or a bat. Of course it is very unlikely that all these animals would live in the same tree at the same time. But these are some of the more common animals that nest in holes in trees, and some of them nest nowhere else.

By looking at a hole in a tree it is difficult to know what is inside, and it is not always safe or possible to poke in your hand to find out. First, watch the tree for an hour or so to see if any of the animals come out to feed. Look around the base of the tree for evidence of feeding or for feathers or bits of fur. Look around the edge of the hole, if possible, for hairs that might become caught in the bark or rough wood.

Last, find a sturdy stick and pound on the base of the tree. If animals do come out, leave as soon as you can so that they will not desert their nest and young.

Robin on nest

Homes on Trees or Shrubs

Birds of many different kinds build nests in the branches of trees and shrubs. From the tiny humming bird, whose nest may be the size of a half dollar, to the osprey, whose nest may weigh a ton, finches, blackbirds, warblers, vireos, thrushes, orioles, mockingbirds, crows and jays, flycatchers, owls, hawks, doves, some of the gulls, some ducks, herons, and cormorants all build nests of one kind or another on the branches of trees or shrubs from ground level to the top of the highest tree.

Some of these birds construct well-built, sturdy nests held together with mud or carefully woven of grasses and other fibrous materials. Others build only crude platforms that oftentimes fail in their purpose, as wind or rain may destroy them and the eggs or young.

Nesting materials consist of a large variety of things. Usually sticks, twigs, sedges, and grasses are used, but some birds use lichens, too, or string, paper, hair, snakeskins, or anything else they can find. Ospreys and eagles have been known to use barbed wire and boards picked up along the river or ocean edge.

Again the size, shape, location, and method of construction help identify bird nests. The easiest way to get to know them is to see the bird on the nest and then, when the nesting season is well over, to examine the nest carefully for details of construction and materials used.

14

Barn swallow on nest

But birds are not the only animals that build nests in the branches of trees. Squirrels and some of the mice also build nests of leaves, sticks, twigs, and grasses on and in branches, from low to the ground to the highest part of the tree. Deer mice may even take over a bird's nest and add a roof to provide the protection they need.

Homes in or on Houses

Some animals make their homes in or on our homes, garages, or barns. The most obvious ones, because of their names, are barn swallow, chimney swifts, barn owls, house finches, and house mice. But robins, phoebes, and wrens will also build nests on window sills, under the eaves, or in other places about the home, and bats, squirrels, or raccoons sometimes find a way into an attic, where they set up housekeeping. Woodchucks, snakes, rats, and skunks also may burrow under a home or other building and make a home, while several kinds of rodents, from deer mice to porcupines, will enter houses if they have the chance. In each case it is not long before the human occupants of the house discover the presence of their wild neighbors.

15

Bullhead on nest

Fish Nests

A walk along the shore of a pond or river in spring will usually result in finding signs of fish. For several kinds make nests in gravel or sand in shallow water, where they lay eggs and guard the nest until the young are hatched. Fish nests are usually round, saucer-shaped depressions on the bottom, from which the fish has fanned away mud or silt. Thus the clean gravel or sand is easy to see on the darker bottom which surrounds it. Sometimes it is possible to see the adult fish guarding the nest. The sunfishes, including large and smallmouthed bass, trout and catfish are a few of the fishes that build nests such as these.

Air Vents

Oftentimes animals such as beavers, muskrats or mink may have a den under a stream bank, or a bear may use a shallow hole or undercut stump or log as a place to spend the winter. It would be possible to overlook these homes except for one thing. In fall or winter, when frost or snow covers the ground, the animal's warm breath rises and forms an air vent in the snow or heavy frost. It is easy to see these "blow holes" and thus discover a home that you overlooked before.

16

Nests on the Ground

Animals make dens or nests underground, and in shrubs and trees to a height of a hundred feet or more above ground. Many of them make their homes on the ground, or only an inch or two deep, or only a few inches above ground.

Animals such as alligators, some of the lizards, some of the snakes, and turtles use rotting vegetation on the ground as a place to lay their eggs and raise their young. Some of the mice, too, build nests of grass in fields or forest edges on the ground, and jack rabbits, deer, elk or antelope use concealed places in high grass or brushy areas as homes as their young are born. Birds such as terns, most of the gulls, most of the ducks and geese, swans, killdeer and other plovers, sandpipers, towhees, ovenbirds, meadow larks, nighthawks, and others build nests or shallow depressions in sand or gravel where they lay and hatch their eggs.

Other animals make their homes in caves or under rocky ledges. Still others will use man-made nesting boxes put out especially for them. But all animals have distinctive kinds of homes and locations for their homes to which they have become adapted over many, many years.

By knowing the kind of home an animal builds or uses and the kind of place in which it is usually found, you have a means of identifying animals by a sign. It is not a sign left by the animal deliberately or by intent, but it is as good proof as you can find that a particular animal made the sign, short of seeing the animal itself. By studying animal homes and how they are built you can learn much about the animal and its habits and characteristics.

Common tern on nest

Raccoon

Doe: White-tailed Deer

Antler-rubbed tree

3   TRACKS, TRAILS, AND OTHER SIGNS

As they move about on the ground from one place to another, most animals leave two kinds of trails. One kind is a visible trail and may consist of footprints in sand, mud, or snow, well-marked runways, slides in mud or snow, droppings scattered along the way, and other evidence that can be seen by man or other animal. The second kind of trail is a scent trail made by scent glands on the animal or by the animal's feet or fur's touching the ground or grass, trees, or shrubs as it moves along. In this chapter only visible tracks, trails, and related signs will be discussed.

Footprints

Footprints of wild animals are easy to find. Look along the beach, around mud puddles in country roads, along streams or lake shores, in snow along field or woodland edges, and other places where the earth is soft enough so that a foot may make an impression in it.

Without even knowing what kind of animal made the track there is much you can find out about the animal and what it was doing. You can tell its approximate size. You can tell whether it was moving slowly or quickly. You can discover which way it was going, and sometimes by following tracks you can tell what the animal eats. You can discover, too, whether the animal usually lives on the ground or whether it normally lives in trees or shrubs.

With practice you can find out what kind of animal made the track, for tracks are almost as distinctive to the experienced outdoorsman as fingerprints are to the FBI.

The first thing to learn in the case of mammals is how to tell the front footprint from the rear, and with animals such as foxes this may be difficult since, in walking, their hind feet come down in the prints made by the front feet. But with rabbits, squirrels, raccoons, opossums, mice, and others that are more commonly found, the hind footprint is larger than the front.

The next thing to look for is how far apart the prints are, for this tells you two things—the size of the animal and whether it was walking, bounding, or running, moving slowly or quickly for its size. The depth of the track and whether it is deeper in front than in back also tells you whether the animal was moving slowly or quickly.

Dogs, foxes, and coyotes may all live in the same area, and their individual tracks are similar to the beginner. By size alone you cannot always tell one animal from another. But the shape of the print and the other characteristics of a series of tracks help you identify the animal.

Careful study of the track, too, will show whether the animal walks flat-footed or on its toes. Skunks, raccoons, beaver and porcupines, bears and man walk on the flat of their feet. Foxes and bobcats walk on their toes, while deer, antelope, elk, or mountain goats walk on their toenails.

Animals that usually live in trees hop or bound along when on the ground. In birds, this means that their tracks will be in pairs, rather than one in front of the other. Sparrows and woodpeckers, for example, hop and leave tracks that are side by side. Quail, grouse, herons or killdeer walk, and their prints are one in front of the other. Some birds, such as robins and other thrushes, both hop and walk, and their tracks frequently prove it.

In mammals, those that live in trees, such as squirrels, leave tracks in which their front feet are side by side, while in rabbit tracks, the front feet are usually one in front of the other. Deer mouse tracks show paired front footprints, while in meadow mouse prints the front feet are on a diagonal.

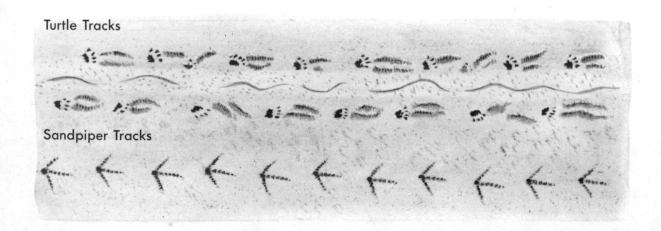

Turtle Tracks

Sandpiper Tracks

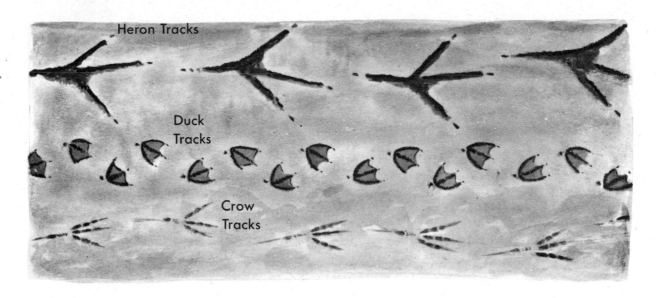

Heron Tracks

Duck Tracks

Crow Tracks

What a Trail Can Tell

By following a trail of individual footprints it is often possible to "read" some fascinating animal stories. You may see where a rabbit stopped to nibble clover or to browse on tree bark; you may see where he was frightened and bounded in a zigzag manner to a nearby wood-chuck hole or bramble. Perhaps he didn't make it, and an owl or fox caught him midway. You may see where a fox walked along, stopping occasionally to sniff at trees, rocks, or shrubs. You see where he stopped to sniff the air, then ran swiftly off at an angle to stop at a mouse-hole to dig out his dinner. You may see where a quail or grouse walked along in the snow, feeding on weed seeds or buds, and suddenly jumped and flew off when frightened by a dead leaf fluttering down or some other sight or sound.

Sometimes it is possible to see where one animal tracked another, or where two animals met in the woods. But experience in reading tracks is important. For once a track is made it may remain for days, and two tracks that cross may have been made hours or more apart. In addition, to know what animal made the track we must also know how fresh the track is.

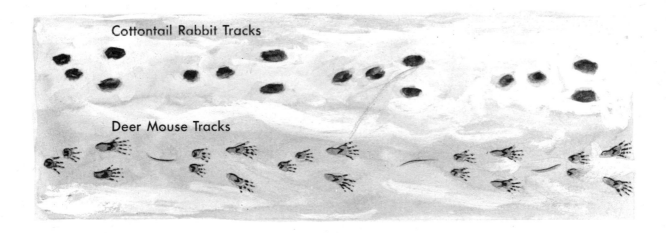

Cottontail Rabbit Tracks

Deer Mouse Tracks

Trails and Runways

Quite often we find runways or trails in the woods or fields where no tracks or footprints are evident. But the well-worn paths made by animals as they walk back and forth to water holes or favorite feeding areas are adequate signs to experienced outdoorsmen. Big game hunters frequently search out these trails and then conceal themselves nearby for an easy shot as the animal comes along. Trappers look for runways made by mink, beaver, muskrats, and other fur bearers and set their traps in these trails. Nature photographers rig up camera traps in similar places to get pictures of wild animals at home. Raccoons, deer, porcupines, woodchucks, mice, and chipmunks frequently have well-defined trails they follow.

Beaver may have similar trails from their pond to nearby clumps of aspens. But many times they make another kind of trail—a water trail or canal along which they float the aspen saplings and branches which they store for winter food.

Other Signs

There are other kinds of signs, too, that may be found in field or forest or along the edge of waterways. Some animals bed down for the night in an open field and, in so doing, mat down the grass in a way that forms an unmistakable sign of what they were doing. Deer beds are often found, and rabbits, too, bed down in this way.

In the western states it is possible, on occasion, to see where a jack rabbit stretched flat on the ground in the slim shade on the north side of a fence post, power pole, or clump of grass, then moved from west to east, staying in the shade as the sun moved from east to west.

Sometimes in dusty roads or patches of bare soil along field or woodland edges you may find shallow depressions in the dust, with footprints of birds leading to and from the saucer-shaped basin. Many birds take dust baths and leave a sign which we may find.

Baltimore oriole dusting

Sidewinder and its tracks

Other animals look for a mudhole to wallow in, as an escape from flies and other insects. Bears often leave such signs, and the buffalo was famous for its wallows.

In areas where deer are common, one often sees the trees where bucks rub their antlers. As new antlers grow each year, they are covered with "velvet" that the deer rubs off when the antlers are full-grown. Many times in the process he also rubs bark off young trees, or at least leaves evidence on the tree of what he has done.

Snakes, Toads, and Turtles

Birds and mammals are not the only animals that leave tracks and trails. Toads, frogs, lizards, and turtles also leave signs as they move through or over sand or mud. These tracks, too, are almost as distinctive as fingerprints, and much the same kinds of stories may be read by studying them.

Rattlesnakes, for example, may leave a straight, unswerving trail as they move slowly along, but when moving quickly their trail zigzags in a series of curves. The trail of a sidewinder in the Southwest shows clearly how the snake got its name. Its trail resembles that which might be left if you rolled a short piece of coiled hose over the sand. It literally jumps along, and leaves an unusual trail behind it.

Animal tracking is fun. It can be exciting. As you become experienced you learn as much from tracks as by watching the animal itself.

Woodchuck whistling

4   SOUND SIGNALS

If you have walked along a woodland edge early on a spring morning, you know that you hear many more birds than you see. If you have wandered beside a bog or wet place at dusk in spring, you know that you hear many more toads and frogs than you ever see. If your neck hairs have bristled at the unexpected and eerie call of a screech owl, or if you heard the weird laugh of a loon, if you have listened to the music of a wood thrush or thrilled to the call of highflying geese, you've heard some of the more interesting sound signals in the world of nature.

Most birds and mammals, some of the reptiles and amphibians, and even some of the fishes make sounds of one sort or another in different ways for different purposes. Through sounds many animals communicate with each other, and if we can intercept those messages and interpret them correctly we can learn much about the animal, what it is doing, and something of why it acts as it does.

Some animal sounds are deliberate, made intentionally for a purpose. Others are the result of some other activity. But all help us to understand more about the animal and its habits.

Just as we make sounds by talking, shouting, whistling, stamping our feet, or clapping our hands to express different feelings, so animals, too, make sounds in different ways.

Many animals use their "voices" to sing, growl, grunt, cry, scream, or howl to express anger, fear, contentment, pain, warnings, or for other purposes. But some animals use their wings, antlers, tails, bills, and feet to make sounds intended to carry a message to another animal.

Bird Songs, Calls, and Sounds

Of all animals, birds probably are best known for their songs, calls, or other sounds. Many of us keep caged birds in our homes so that we may enjoy their songs and music. But few caged-bird songs can ever compete with wild bird music, as these animals use their voices to express contentment with life or to defend their home territories against others.

24

Most bird songs or other sounds reach a peak during the mating season and fulfill a definite function in the life cycle of the bird. The robin in the treetop, the bluebird on the fence post, the meadow lark on the wire, the song sparrow in the rosebush, or the oriole trilling from the elm, all are saying, in effect, "This area around here is mine—all other males of my species, keep out." And if another male does venture in to cross that invisible line marking the first bird's territory, the characteristic song changes to a call of anger as the intruder is attacked and chased away.

Some birds use other means of making sounds that are related to mating and defense of their territory. Flickers often will drum on a metal rain gutter or metal boxes on power poles where, apparently, the purpose is to make a noise. Grouse perch on a dead log and beat the air with their wings, making a drumming or booming noise that somewhat resembles the sound of a gasoline engine being started on a cold day 'way off in the distance. Prairie chickens use their "voice" to boom, but usually start their mating procedure by beating the ground with their feet in a pattering dance that may cover considerable ground before they stop.

When young are hatched, other sounds may be heard which have different meanings. Newly hatched songbirds in the nest have a distinctive hunger call that helps start a reaction in the adult bird to feed them. At the same time many adult birds have a warning chirp that they use to quiet the young, should apparent danger threaten. These sounds may be heard as one stands quietly near the nests of robins, catbirds, thrashers, jays, or sparrows.

With birds where the young leave the nest within hours after they are hatched, the females have a definite warning cluck that causes the young to stand or lie motionless for several minutes at a time. In some cases it is even possible to pick up a young bird in your hand. A second call note from the female seems to indicate that possible danger is over, and the young once again walk around seeking food. These sounds and resulting reactions may be heard and seen with quail, grouse, pheasants, killdeer and other plovers, rails, and other birds.

Many birds have an alarm note that is quite different from other sounds they make. The robin on the lawn, the jay in the woods, the heron in the marsh, the duck on the pond, the gulls or sandpipers along the water's edge, the hawk on its nest, or the loon on the lake all make distinctive sounds of alarm or displeasure when approached too closely by man or wild animal. These sounds vary from a scarcely audible "chip" to a raucous squawk, from a shrill whistle to a trembling laugh, as the birds run, swim, or fly away.

Quite often on a spring or fall night one hears the sounds of birds flying over. The experienced naturalist can frequently tell with considerable accuracy exactly what species he hears as the birds chip or chirp in their migratory flight. To most of us these are only bird sounds in the night, but they are also sound signals that let us know that birds are flying over. Many times, though, we can recognize the honks of geese, the quacks of ducks, the whistles of sandpipers, and the chips of warblers or thrushes. For these are birds that fly at night and apparently keep up a more or less constant communication so that they may stay together in a flock.

During the spring, when waves of migrating warblers move through, these same sounds may be heard as small flocks of birds go from tree to tree, but ever in a northerly direction.

Another sound that is distinctive and different and made for another purpose is the feeding call of ducks and geese. If there is any sound in nature that resembles a large room full of

25

Feeding ducks make distinctive sounds that attract others

Flicker pounding on rain drain to send a sound signal

people gossiping and chattering, it is that made by a flock of brant or Canada geese as they dabble and feed on bay or lake. Mallards, black ducks, widgeon, teal, and pintails all "talk" back and forth as they feed on lake or pond, and this feeding chatter is a different sound from others made by the birds.

While some sounds are the result of other activities, they nonetheless carry a message to one who listens and understands. Woodpeckers feed by pounding their chisel-like bills into tree bark and wood in search of insect larvae. They also chisel out holes in dead trees in which they make their nests.

The resulting sound may be heard over a considerable distance on a still day, and the intensity of the sound plus the rhythm and interval between sounds tells the listener which one of the woodpeckers he hears. From the small downy woodpecker with its rapid tattoo to the crow-sized pileated with its slower, resounding pounding, different woodpeckers may be identified by the rhythm of their hammering.

Mammal Sounds

Sound signals made by wild mammals are not so commonly heard as those made by birds. Mammals are more wary of man, and many of them are active only at night. Usually we must get out of town, out to the fields and woods, marsh, or pond to hear mammals communicating with each other or with us.

Mammals, like birds, make sounds in various ways for different reasons. Some sounds are deliberate, others accidental. All of them can tell us quite a bit about the animal itself.

As with birds, many mammal sound signals are connected with the mating process and serve to attract a mate, to challenge other males to fight for a mate, or to warn other males to keep their distance. These signals are made in different ways, too—with "voice," by stamping feet, by rattling antlers against bush or tree, and in other ways.

27

Of the larger animals that inhabit wilder parts of the country, the moose and elk are well-known for their bugling calls which may be heard for a mile or more. These calls by the bulls during the mating season are intended to attract the attention of a cow, and at the same time they serve as a challenge or warning to other bulls. Deer rattle their antlers against saplings or bushes and, on occasion, paw the ground or stamp their feet.

Mammals, too, make other sounds for different purposes. A fawn may bleat to show that it is hungry. Any of us who have ever stood on or near a beaver house have heard the whimpering cry of the young inside, probably indicating hunger or fear. The squirrel's chatter of anger when disturbed, the rabbit's scream of terror when caught by fox or owl, the purr of a bobcat after a meal of mice, the howl of coyote, or the yap of a fox, all are sound signals indicating a feeling of one sort or another. Mice and chipmunks sing with a warbling tremor, bats use voices that are pitched so high that we cannot hear them to find food or avoid obstacles in the dark. Bears growl to warn their young of danger; beaver and muskrats splash the water, and others of their kind are warned. Wolves have a distinctive howl that shows they are closing in for the kill, and raccoons or woodchucks vocally indicate their displeasure if disturbed by man or beast. An opossum makes a hissing noise when unhappy, as do rats or mink.

All mammals apparently have the power of voice, some using this power more than others. But each sound may carry a message that tells a story to him who listens with understanding ears.

Spring peepers are easily identified by their call

Grouse drumming

Imitating Animal Sounds

Over the years man has shown a remarkable ability to imitate animals. In the early days these imitations were necessary to obtain food and clothing, and the American Indian was skilled at calling animals up to him for an easier shot with bow and arrow.

Thus deer calls were made that resembled the bleat of the fawn and attracted the doe. Moose calls imitated the bugling of the bull, and elk calls were similarly designed. Beaver were called by knocking against a canoe with paddle or knife, and turkey calls that imitated the gobble of the male or the feeding notes of the flock were made from wood and leaves.

Those crude but effective imitation calls were a far cry from the now-illegal electronic devices used to attract ducks to the hunter's blind. Sound recordings were made of feeding ducks, and during the hunting season they were played back over loud amplifiers. Responding to the sound, birds flocked in to join in the feed, only to find hunters waiting. But man-operated duck calls are legal, and in the hands and mouth of a master they truly sound like ducks.

Sound signals are among the more interesting signs of nature. Understanding them adds much to the enjoyment of the outdoors. They tell stories of animal life that are told in no other way.

California Woodpecker

Porcupines frequently gnaw
tool handles

5 FEEDING SIGNS

Since all animals must eat in order to survive, feeding signs often tell us that certain animals live in a given area, although the animals themselves are never seen. In many cases these signs are distinctive and very different, one from the other, so that the story they tell is easy to read.

Signs of feeding take many forms. Gnawed bark on trees, browsed twigs or branches, shells of acorns and other nuts, bits of fur or feathers, skeletons or carcasses, holes in trees or holes in the ground, floating vegetation in a pond or lake, closely clipped grass, piles of mussel shells, ridges in the earth, jumping fish—these and many more are feeding signs of mouse or moose, woodcock or woodchuck, shrike or shrew, bass or beaver.

Plant-eating Animals

Signs of animals that eat plant life in one form or another are easy to find, if one looks for them, and many times such signs can be found in the back yard or garden.

Rabbits, squirrels, mice, raccoons, opossums, muskrats, and even deer, in some places, will invade a garden plot to find an easy supply of food. Rabbits are fond of new tender lettuce or cabbage, and sometimes nibble it right back to ground level. In so doing they leave a distinctive sign on the edges of leaves. They also will eat lawn plants, such as clover, and on occasion in winter or early spring will gnaw bark of apple and other fruit trees.

31

Mice, too, during a cold winter will tunnel under the snow and girdle the bark of young trees and ornamental shrubs, doing much damage in the process. Field mice often feed on grasses and other plant matter in the yard or garden, and deer mice leave telltale signs as they gnaw through acorns or other nuts. These same animals frequently visit bird feeding stations to eat sunflower and other seeds placed there for birds. They usually feed after dark, and the bird watcher who fills his feeders late in the afternoon only to find them empty at dawn, would do well to watch for mice or even rats.

Raccoons and muskrats, if the garden is near water, sometimes invade cornfields. Raccoons are particularly fond of the new tender ears of corn, and break down the stalks in order to get them. Muskrats will chew off young stalks and take them back to their houses or burrows. They, too, will eat the new ears as they form.

Squirrels like corn, but they will also eat nuts and fruit. They are known to dig up the bulbs of tulips and other flowers, and often visit back yard bird feeders during the winter. Opossums are fond of fruits and some garden vegetables and are common back yard visitors in some places. Deer, too, visit gardens, where they eat a variety of foods from new grown tulips or daffodils and other flowering plants and shrubs to peas, beans, lettuce, cabbage, corn, beet tops, and carrots. They even dig out root crops for a meal, or eat apples and other fruits as well as browse on the growth of tender foliage.

A combination of signs often will tell us that animals have visited our garden. Marks of teeth on the plants or plant parts are good indicators, but tracks in the ground and droppings are confirming signs.

Several kinds of birds are frequent back yard visitors, feeding on new shoots, fruits, and other plant parts. Mourning doves like the first shoots of peas or beans, and robins are notorious for eating cherries, blackberries, and similar fruit. Thrushes flock to trees such as dogwood and viburnums, and waxwings will clean the fruit from a fire thorn in a remarkably short time. Blackbirds infest cornfields in late summer in some places, and pheasants, quail, or sparrows may be seen eating weed seeds in fall or winter.

Gull eating clam

Terns feed on small fish chased to the surface by larger fish

Even box or wood turtles may visit the yard to eat tomatoes, berries, or mushrooms, and in some places bears are nocturnal visitors to garbage can, apple tree or beehive.

Some of these same signs and others, too, may be found in the wild. It's a common sight, while walking through the woods, to find a stump, log, or rock that serves a squirrel as a dining perch. Piles of nut and fruit seed shells quickly show what the animal eats. In fall one may be bewildered, at first, at seeing mushrooms carefully placed on the branches of a spruce or hemlock, almost as if some playful child were decorating a Christmas tree. But red squirrels store fungus plants in this way as a future supply of food, and close examination will show their tooth marks along the edges of the mushroom caps.

Campers in the north country or certain mountain areas know well the feeding signs of porcupines if they leave an ax or canoe paddle within reach of these rodents. Hikers in bear country sometimes find holes in the ground where these animals have dug up food stored by squirrels or mice. Beaver-chewed stumps, logs, or branches are unmistakable signs of these large rodents.

There may be signs in ponds or lakes that are good indications that several animals are present. In some places muddy water is a good sign that carp are rooting on the bottom in search of water plants. Floating vegetation may indicate that muskrats have been feeding, and in wilder places a combination of muddy water and floating plant remains may show that a moose recently was finding a meal there.

One of the more interesting signs of feeding is that of the California woodpecker. This bird eats acorns as part of its diet, and it has an unusual way of keeping them for future use. It chisels small holes in the bark of trees, and wedges acorns so well into them that it is hard to remove them.

Great Horned Owl searching for food

Cottontail
Rabbit

Opossum

Deer Mouse

House mouse leaving signs of feeding

Animals That Eat Other Animals

Animals that eat other animals range from the tiny shrew, smaller than your thumb, to a bear that may weigh several hundred pounds. In between are other mammals and also birds, fish, reptiles, and amphibians. These animals eat a wide variety of animal foods and, in so doing, many of them leave distinctive and interesting signs.

Again, some of these animals are more or less common park or back yard residents or visitors, and their value in helping to control insects, rodents, and other garden pests is often evident from their signs of feeding.

Small holes in the ground are sometimes the result of birds' probing for grubs, and the ground beneath a nest may be littered with the shells of beetles, or wings of other insects upon which birds feed.

It is possible, too, to find the pellets of an owl—the undigested fur and bones of mice, which the owl spits out. These signs show that an owl may roost there, but they also show what small mammals live nearby.

Ridges in the lawn or garden may indicate that a mole has been tunneling in search of grubs or worms, and a snail shell or two may show that a shrew has found a meal. The sudden disappearance of goldfish from the garden pool may well be a sign that a heron has found food, and a lack of activity at a bird feeder may be the result of a hawk perched in a nearby tree or even on the TV antenna. The excited chirping of a robin may show that a jay has found the nest and eggs, or the raucous squawk of a jay may be an indication that a cat lurks in the garden in search of a bird. It may also show that an owl, crow, or snake is nearby, looking for an easy meal.

Many of these same feeding signs may be found in the wild—out on the edge of town, in the woods or fields, along ponds or streams, and in wilder places. There are others, too, that show that different animals have been feeding and of what their food consists.

Along rivers, ponds, and marshes, piles of clam or mussel shells may be the sign of a muskrat dining room, while clam shells scattered along the sea beach, coastal highways, or on flat roofs or paved driveways are a good sign of herring gulls. These birds drop clams and crabs from a hundred feet or more in the air to crack the shell on a hard surface to get at the meat inside. Where human home or roadway is handy to beach or mud flat, man-made surfaces are frequently used by gulls. Automobile accidents have occurred as motorists attempt to dodge falling clams, and seashore home owners often must stay indoors or seek shelter from these bird-bombers.

While walking along the shore of ocean, bay, or lake, one frequently sees signs of fish feeding. These signs take different forms and are helpful to the fisherman if he interprets them correctly. A school of small fish jumping or skittering along the surface often indicates that they are pursued by larger fish, and sometimes these small fish in their flight jump out of the water to come down on the shore. Large flocks of gulls hovering and diving in one area may be a sign that large game fish have slashed through a school of smaller fish. The gulls feed on the remains of the fish's feeding, and fishermen usually hurry to such a spot to try for the game fish. Petrels hovering over the ocean also may show that fish are feeding, and pelicans or gannets diving from a considerable height shows that their food is close to the surface.

Screech owls leave unmistakable signs of feeding in the form of pellets

Owl pellets and field mouse bones, which they contain

A single track in mud along a lake or river may show that a heron waited there for a frog or fish, and pellets composed of shells, bones, and scales along the shore are signs that gulls or herons have coughed up the undigested parts of their mollusk or fish meal.

Signs in fields and forest are equally distinctive. Small holes in the ground may be the sign of a skunk's digging out a mouse nest or anthill or be the result of a fox's digging for its food. In western states badgers leave their mark as they dig for gophers, ground squirrels, or mice, and in bear country torn decayed logs show where this animal has searched for grubs. Bear scratches on power poles may show that bears were misled by the hum of wires to think they had found a bee tree, and woodpeckers, too, are known to chisel holes in poles in search of food.

The remains of birds, rabbits, squirrels, or fish may be the sign of a fox, a mink, a hawk, or an owl, and other signs should be studied to decide which one left the sign. A songbird or frog impaled on a thorn or twig is an indication of a shrike, and some hawks, too, wedge their prey in a tree crotch to hold it while they eat it. Some animals can eat only part of their prey at one time and cover the remainder of the carcass with leaves or grass to hide it until they again are hungry. Weasels are known to store up mice, as do some of the owls, and these storehouses, if found, are excellent signs of animal feeding.

Animal droppings are frequently used by professional naturalists to study the feeding habits of animals. First, the droppings themselves in many cases are almost a sure sign of a particular animal. Insect, bone, fur, scale, or feather particles in the droppings or "scats" show what the animal has been eating. By studying large numbers of these signs the year-round pattern of feeding habits may be determined.

Thus feeding signs may provide important information to many people. Fishermen, hunters, trappers, photographers, zoologists rely on it for the success of their endeavors.

Mink have musk glands which they use to send scent signals

6   SCENT SIGNALS

One of the most interesting and perhaps least understood methods of animal communication is the scent sign which one animal leaves and which may be noted by another. The reason it is not understood by man undoubtedly is that we cannot smell the scent, in most cases, and must rely on visual observations and study the reactions of animals to it.

Scent signals and signs may be either accidental or deliberate. The chipmunk that leaves a scent trail which a weasel may follow has no intention of communicating with the weasel. But the weasel that is pursued by a larger animal gives off a musky odor as a defensive weapon aimed at discouraging capture by his enemy. The deer whose scent glands in its legs leave a trail which a coyote or wolf may follow does not deliberately send a message to his enemy. The purpose of this accidental trail may be to leave a sign for other deer to follow.

Observations and study by trained and experienced naturalists show that scent signs carry many different messages from one animal to another. Animal odors not only identify the animal itself but also seem to show its physical condition and state of mind. They apparently carry messages of love, fear, hate, anger, and other emotions, which other animals seem to understand quite easily.

39

Left: Red fox at scent post

Beaver attracted by castor

Ernest Thompson Seton, in his *Lives of Game Animals,* tells of an experience with caribou. He was standing near a caribou trail watching a cow amble along. The wind was blowing from the animal toward him when it suddenly changed, so that she caught his scent. She quickly jumped to one side and ran off. A short time later other cows came along the trail, and again the wind blew from the animals toward the observer and there was little chance that they would smell him. But when they reached the point where the first caribou had jumped in fear, they, too, jumped to one side and ran away. It seemed reasonable to assume that the scent trail of the first animal carried a message of fear to others, which, upon receiving it, reacted to it.

Animal Signposts

Signposts are used by several kinds of animals. These information spots may be trees, bushes, rocks, or hummocks, and are used in much the same way that dogs use fire hydrants, fence posts, or power poles in city or suburb.

Bullheads use their barbels to ''smell'' for food

Male cottontail rabbits are known to have favorite spots where they stop in their wanderings to rub their chins on tree trunks, leaving their individual scents and perhaps some other message.

Black bears have their signposts—special trees which they visit. They sniff around the tree, then reach up and scratch the bark with their sharp claws. Sometimes they bite out large chunks of wood and bark, then wander on. One writer tells of an experience with bears at a log cabin he owned deep in the woods. When he first visited his cabin one spring he found that a bear, or bears, had used a twelve-inch pine post that supported the cabin porch roof as a signpost. In one spring the bears had nearly torn the post apart. He replaced it with a new one, and on his next visit a month or so later found it, too, was scratched and ripped apart. That same thing happened three times in one season.

Foxes, wolves and coyotes have their information spots, as do dogs in town. They visit these points, sniff carefully, add their message and walk on. What information is exchanged at these points? No one knows for sure, but foxes, apparently without a problem in the world, have been seen to visit a signpost, sniff it carefully, growl and in other ways show fear or anger, then answer in kind and walk off on stiff legs, looking back from time to time.

Beavers, too, have places along pond banks or stream edges where they leave a message for others to read. These animals make small piles of mud pies which are scented with a subtance called castoreum. These messages may well be "love letters in the mud" from one animal to another. Muskrats, also, leave scent signs along their trails or on their feeding platforms, perhaps for the same purpose, perhaps for another.

Various animals have scent glands with which they leave a trail similar to the deer and caribou. The peccary or javelina, the wild pig of the Southwest, has a scent gland on its rump which rubs against the shrubbery under which it walks. The kangaroo rat has a scent gland between its shoulders that gives off a waxy substance as a scent signal, and bighorn sheep have a gland near their eyes that leaves a scent as they feed. The mountain goat has a rubbery sort of gland behind each horn that is especially active during the mating season. This gland gives off its scent as the animal rubs its head on brush. All the deer have two sets of glands, one in each rear hoof and one set higher up on the side of each hind leg. The opossum and marten have scent glands which they rub on tree branches as they climb, leaving a story for others to read.

Other animals use their scents as methods of defense, and the message they carry to man or beast may be strong indeed. The striped and the spotted skunks are well known for their scent signals, and weasels and mink give off a musky odor which, although not sprayed as with a skunk, is nonetheless effective in defense.

The tiny shrew, the smallest of our mammals, also gives off an odor as a means of defense, and some turtles carry such descriptive names as "stink pots" because of the musky scent they give off when captured.

All of these animals, then, send signals of one sort or another by scent. But the word "communication" means receiving as well as sending a message. Most animals receive scent signals with their noses. And the messages they receive cause them to react in different ways.

Many animals use their powers of smell to find food. All of the meat-eating mammals probably depend more on their noses to find a meal than on any other of their senses. The weasel that stalks the mouse, the bear that digs out the grubs, the fox, coyote, or badger that digs out the ground squirrel nest, and the wolf that pursues the deer, the fisher that catches the squirrel, the mink that kills the duck, and the bobcat that feeds on the grouse all depend upon sensitive noses, at least in part, to find their food. The trails left by the prey were unintentional scent signals—but signals, nevertheless—to other animals.

Cottontail rabbit leaving a scent signal

Skunks are famous for scent signals

Snakes, too, leave scent trails and follow scents left by others. They use their noses to smell, but in addition have another means of following a scent. Their forked tongues are believed to be used to pick up scent particles which are carried to two cavities in the roof of the mouth, and thus they may find the food they need for survival.

Many snakes have distinctive odors that come from scent glands, and these scents are used when the snake is annoyed or during the mating season as a means of communication with the opposite sex.

Some of the fishes use their power of smell to find food, and fisherman use this knowledge in selecting baits. Catfish are well known for seeming to prefer bait having strong odors, and everything from dried blood to slightly decayed chicken innards are used to catch these fish. When they are hungry, some fish strike first and then taste their food. Trout will jump at a fly, or bass or perch will grab a passing minnow. But at other times these fish nose food particles for a minute or more before taking it in their mouths. Fish that feed chiefly at night depend largely on smell to find food. Fish have nostrils with which they smell, but some of them have barbels with which they may also pick up scent or taste sensations.

Scents and smells are an important means of communication to animals. Bears may use this means to mark their territory and warn others. Deer use scent to send different messages and also to help them stay together in the herd. Members of the dog family use smells to exchange information, while skunks or weasels use scent to defend themselves. Wolverines protect their food supply with a vile-smelling scent.

There is much yet to be learned about this subject. The problem is that we cannot smell many of the messages, and animals cannot tell us what they really mean. All we can do is make careful observations and then try to understand from the way animals react.

43

Kingbird attacking a crow

Robin attacking own reflection in glass

7   TOUCH SIGNALS

Touch signals among animals are quite common, and most of us probably have seen them or felt them in one way or another. One robin attacking another in the garden and a wren attacking a cat that gets too near the nest are examples of this kind of communication between animals.

Touch signals are made with different parts of an animal's body, depending upon the animal. Foxes bite; birds peck with their bills, strike with their wings, or bomb with their excrement; deer kick or push with their antlers; porcupines strike with quill-covered tails, and alligators, too, use their strong tails to strike an enemy. Rabbits kick with their strong hind legs, and bears may hug or scratch with their front legs or claws. Some snakes strike with their noses, others with poison-filled fangs. Bobcats and mountain lions strike with their sharp front claws, and mountain sheep, goats, or buffalo butt with their hard heads and horns.

45

Why Animals Use Touch Signals

Animals may use touch signals for several reasons, but mostly for defending themselves, defending their territory or mates, defending their young or fighting for a mate.

Many animals, especially birds, mammals, and some of the fish, establish territories around their nests or dens. The purpose of this territory is to provide living space for the animal where it can have some degree of privacy and where it can obtain food more easily for its young and for itself.

Territories, as such, vary in size depending upon the animal. A fox or wolf may have a territory measured in square miles, while a robin's territory may be measured in square feet, less than an acre. A wren may defend an area only twenty to thirty feet on each side around its hole, and gulls or other birds that nest in colonies may have territories that are not much larger than eight or ten feet on a side. Purple martins that nest several families at a time in a box three feet wide, long, and high may defend only their cubicles, which are six inches by six inches by eight inches.

But in any case these animals have a territory or back yard of their own whose boundaries they recognize. If other animals, usually males of the same species, come too close, the intruder is attacked for the purpose of driving it away.

Deer delivering a touch message to a coyote

46

The animal on the receiving end of this means of communication seems to know, in many cases, that it is the intruder, and sometimes it will defend itself by fighting back and sometimes it flies or runs away.

Some birds, especially those that nest in colonies, such as gulls or terns, will band together in an effort to drive away an intruder in the colony. Anyone who has ventured too close to a nesting tern on a sea beach or neighboring dunes knows what happens. One pair of terns, the first to be approached, flies into the air and utters shrill cries of alarm. They swoop down on the intruder and often hit him with their beaks or wings, and very quickly other birds in the colony join in the fight. They continue this aerial bombing until the unwanted visitor leaves and crosses an invisible line surrounding the colony. The birds then return to their nests.

It is interesting that many of these birds that defend the area around their nests from intruders feed together with them with little regard for one another. The same terns or gulls or even robins that drive others from their territories may be seen feeding close to each other with no semblance of the hostile attitude they show when on their home territory.

Gulls, though, will often fight each other for food and even try to steal food from other birds. In so doing a gull will dive, peck, and strike with its wings in an effort to force another bird to drop the food it has found along the beach or on the water.

Fishermen use this characteristic of gulls to free themselves of birds that flock after their boats and sometimes alight on the boats to steal fish which are being cleaned. The method used is to tie small fish to opposite ends of a three-foot-long piece of string and to throw the fish overboard. A gull swoops down, takes one of the fish in its bill and flies away. Another gull usually grabs the dangling second fish, and the fun begins. The whole flock leaves the boat to fight the first two gulls for food.

Eagles, too, are notorious for this characteristic of attacking other birds in order to get food the first bird has captured. Ospreys and gulls are frequent victims of eagles, and usually drop the fish before actual contact is made. But if they persist in holding the fish, eagles sometimes strike them with their talons.

Defending Young

Closely related to defense of the territory is defense of the young. Most birds and mammals and some of the fishes, for a short time at least, will defend their young by fighting, even at the expense of their own lives.

Even human beings are oftentimes on the receiving end of these touch signals, sometimes with very unhappy results. A few years ago a family of touring easterners parked their large and expensive sedan along the road in a western national park to photograph a cow bison grazing on the hillside. What they didn't know was that they had stopped between the cow and the calf. Fortunately no one was injured when the cow butted the car and turned it over, but the car had to be towed away.

A well-known nature photographer was once on the receiving end of the touch signal of an osprey. He was high in a spruce, photographing a nest in the top of a neighboring tree, when one of the adult hawks attacked him from behind, knocking him from his perch.

Quite a few hunters, nature photographers, and other outdoor hobbyists have spent many an unpleasant hour up a tree to avoid receiving a touch signal from a bear or moose. In some cases intercepting a message sent through animal communications is fun and interesting, but not when delivered in person by an animal weighing up to half a ton or more.

Even some of the fishes—bass, bluegills, and catfish or bullhead, for example—will defend the nest, and, for a short time, perhaps their young against undesirable visitors. By watching the nests of these fish it is often possible to see them attack and drive off, or attempt to drive off, other fish that swim too close to the nest. The bass will use its teeth to deliver the message and the catfish has its spiny fin. Some fish use their tails to force a flow of water against the side of another, where the signal is received by the second fish's lateral line, a sense organ that runs along the side of the fish.

Fighting for a Mate

Some animals, such as deer, elk, moose, mountain goats, and bighorn sheep, are known for their message delivered by head, horn, or antler. Bull elk, for example, round up several cows when mating season approaches. In the process they may run into the problem of another bull who has the same idea. Many times young bulls will challenge an older animal to fight for his collection of females, and a head-to-head conflict takes place. The animals push and shove, cracking their antlers together, until one gives in and backs away.

Male pheasants, also, usually have a number of females in their "families" and during the spring months must on occasion fight for their rights. Much of the time the fight is nothing more than bluff, as one bird lowers its head, sticks out its wings, and prances toward the other. But pheasants have spurs on the backs of their legs with which they can deliver a rather strong message if the need arises.

Pheasants use their spurs as weapons

Black bear punishing cub

Animals that live together sometimes fight over other things than territory or mates. They may fight over food, a favorite perch, or other things. Rather soon they learn from experience which other animals in the group are stronger or weaker than they, and what biologists call a "peck order" is set up. One animal is at the top—it dominates the others. Animal number two is dominated by the first, but it dominates those farther down the ladder. Finally we come to the animal at the bottom of the heap, who is "picked on" by all the rest and who has no animal below it to pick on in turn. These animals fight back and forth to raise their places on the ladder.

Teaching Young

Some animals use touch signals in the training of their young. Female bears use their strong front legs to swat a cub which moves too slowly along the trail, which wanders away from the family group, or which gets into other mischief with its brother or sister. Foxes snap at young with their teeth, pinching rather than biting, to teach a cub a lesson, and bobcats use their paws to punish a kitten that gets out of hand. Birds will cover their young with their wings and the young react by lying down in the nest. Opossums use their tails, deer use their noses, and skunks and mink use their mouths to signal by touch to their offspring.

Most of these touch signals are deliberate on the part of the animal involved. The animal shows some degree of intent in its communication with others. But such an animal as a snake that suddenly strikes when startled does so through reflex action more probably than through intent.

Animals, then, communicate with other wild animals and with man through touch signals. As far as man is concerned it is usually safer to observe the signals from a distance than personally to be on the receiving end.

Prairie chickens' mating dance

Antelope alert for danger

8 SIGHT SIGNALS

Probably the best way that we have of understanding wild animals, their habits, and their individual characteristics is through visual observation. In other words, we watch them and their actions and then draw certain conclusions as to what we think they are doing and why. In a sense, the animal is communicating with us through sight signals.

First, we can recognize animals for what they are by size, shape, color, and other characteristics. We can tell a deer from a deer mouse or a gopher from a gopher tortoise by sight. But we can also tell a male oriole from its mate, a young robin from an adult, a fawn from a buck deer, or a buck deer from a doe. We can tell the species of an animal, the age of some animals, and the sex of some animals just by looking at them.

There is more we can tell, too, depending upon our experience with animals. If we see a skunk raise its tail or stamp its feet we know it's time to move away or suffer the consequences. When we get close enough to a moose to see him raise the hackle hairs on his neck, we know that if we are smart we will move back to shelter of some sort.

If we are stalking a deer with bow or camera and see it feeding, we know that slow, careful movements probably will not startle it. But if we see it flash its "flag" we know that it will soon lift its head for a look around. That is our cue to "freeze" in our tracks and remain motionless.

51

Animals signal their intentions or their attitudes with their feet, their tails, their ears, their hair, the way they hold their heads, and in other ways that form sight signals for us or for other animals. Some of these signals show a degree of intent, as in the case of the skunk or the moose. In other cases the signal may be the result of a reflex action, and in many cases the signal is a definite accident.

The cottontail feeding at night along the field edge or roadside does not intend to communicate with the horned owl in the tree. In fact, the rabbit tries not to advertise his existence in any way whatever. But the owl sees movement and swoops down on the rabbit.

The bass or sunfish swimming close to the surface has no intention of communicating with the osprey flying overhead or the great blue heron standing in the shallows. But the movement of the fish sends a message to hawk or heron that that bird understands.

Many animals obtain their food through sight signals or signs. The bass themselves and the sunfish, trout, pike, perch, and other fish strike at movement, color, or shape on and in the water that indicates or resembles food. Sometimes they strike in anger or curiosity, sometimes because they are hungry. Many times when they taste what they have taken in their mouths they immediately reject it, or try to if there is no hook involved.

Birds, too, of several kinds feed by sight. Gulls, terns, pelicans, kingfishers, and others dive to capture food they see in the water. Some ducks dive to the bottom to feed on plant life while others pursue fish or other aquatic animals. Warblers catch insects on the wing, as do swallows and flycatchers, and road runners in the West pursue lizards or toads across the desert. Other birds feed on seeds of various sorts, which they find by sight.

Lizards, toads, and frogs use their long tongues to pick insects they see out of the

Male flicker showing its mustache

Squid squirting "ink" to defend itself

air, while hawks use remarkable powers of sight to swoop down from great heights and seize their prey.

Mice use their noses to find food, but recent experiments show that they depend upon sight in some cases.

In some areas of the Northwest, forest tree seeds were eaten in large numbers by mice. So many seeds were devoured that a sufficient quantity of trees would not grow. Wildlife biologists discovered that if the seeds were dyed different colors the mice would pass them by and not recognize them as food.

Similar experiments have shown that birds and fish see certain colors and color combinations and recognize them in one degree or another. Some birds, for example, may capture a brightly colored wasp and eat it. They immediately spit it out because of an unpleasant taste. They soon learn to reject other wasps and even have rejected edible food that had the same color or color combinations. Other insects, too, are recognized by color as having an unpleasant taste, and birds leave them alone.

Another series of experiments has shown that fish learn to disregard a lure which they have seen several times, but will hit a new one they see for the first time. Color, shape, and movement were the combination of sight signals to which the fish reacted by taking or disregarding lures.

Color Recognition

Color recognition undoubtedly plays a part in birds' recognizing the opposite sex, but many details are not completely understood by scientists. In most of our songbirds and ducks,

53

the sexes are very different in color and color combinations. Usually the male is more brightly colored and the female and young are drab in comparison.

With some birds it is impossible for us to tell male from female unless the bird is held in the hand. Robins, jays, gulls, terns, and shore birds are birds where the sexes are similar in appearance. Other birds have only small distinguishing marks that enable us to tell a male from female in the field. The male kingfisher, for example, has one reddish band on its breast, while the female has two. The male downy woodpecker has a red spot on the back of its head where the female has none, and the male flicker has a black mustache which the female does not have.

Color evidently does play some part in birds' recognition of sex, or how can we account for the display of brightly colored feathers by the male during the mating season? Robins and meadow larks are seen to strut and show off their bright breasts, and some of the male warblers flash their bright plumage when courting a mate.

An experiment with flickers did show that the mustache of the male played an important part in one bird's recognizing another. A pair of flickers was seen to be getting ready to build a nest and set up housekeeping. The female bird was trapped and an artificial mustache was attached to her head with household cement. When she was released and flew back to the male he immediately attacked her as if she were another male that had invaded his territory.

White-tailed deer "waving its flag"

Redstart displaying bright colors

But the story had a happy ending, since the female was again trapped and the mustache removed. Soon thereafter the two birds resumed their preparations for raising a family.

Another experiment based on the reaction of a bird to a sight signal was tried with robins. A small mirror was placed upright on the ground near a robin nest. The male robin walked by and saw his reflection, immediately attacking his image as if it were another male robin. When the mirror was moved outside his territory the attacks stopped. This experiment also explains the reason for birds flying at picture windows or shiny automobile chrome. They are not "crazy," as news writers would have us suppose. They are merely fighting what they see as another male.

Some animals soon learn to recognize enemies by sight. A flock of crows will mob an owl they find perched in a tree. A jay will dive bomb a cat, and a kingbird will see a crow, hawk, or other large bird approaching and attempt to drive it off. A flock of birds at a feeder will dive for cover at the sight of a hawk, and a snake climbing a tree toward a catbird nest sets up an immediate reaction on the part of the bird.

A sunfish or perch darts for cover as a pike glides by, and turtles slide off a log into the water when frightened. An antelope can sight an enemy at considerable distance, and the white hairs on his rump are erected, showing his reaction to this sight signal. Other antelope see the white flash and receive a sight message indicating possible danger. The white "flag" of the white-tailed deer also flashes a warning which others may read.

Killdeer and other shore birds, as well as grouse, use an interesting sight signal to defend their young or their nest. When an unwelcome visitor wanders too close to the nest, the female flies or runs off and stops a few feet away. Oftentimes she flies toward the intruder to land between him and the nest.

She then flutters and flops, dragging one wing as if it were broken, attempting to lead the intruder away from the nest. When successful, and the source of possible danger is some distance away, the bird quickly recovers from its feigned injury and flies back to its nest.

These are only some of the ways that animals send and receive sight signals as warnings to others, defending their young, finding food and finding a mate.

There is much still to be discovered about this means of communication and only many, many more observations will solve some of the riddles. One purpose of this book has been to show how animals communicate with others and with man with the hope that readers will become sufficiently interested to help find answers to some of the questions. For intercepting and interpreting animal signs, sounds and other signals is fun it itself. It also adds much to the enjoyment of other outdoor hobbies.

Killdeer feigning injury

Index

PRAIRIE DOG

SCREECH OWL

RABBIT TRACKS

RUFFED GROUSE

WHITE-TAILED DEER

BEAVER

GREAT HORNED OWL

RED FOX

WOOD DUCK

RACCOON TRACKS

REDHEADED WOODPECKER

MEADOWLARK

BASS SUNFISH

FIELD MOUSE

BLUEBIRD

STRIPED SKUNK

WOODCHUCK

BOX TURTLE

PORCUPINE

BROWN TROUT

BLACK BEAR

RATTLESNAKE

FLICKER

RED SQUIRREL

DATE DUE